BED BUGS

Tim Colli

Illustrated by Jam

Titles in Horror Hotel:

NIGHTMARE MAN
TIM COLLINS & ABBY RYDER

WALL CRAWLERS
TIM COLLINS & JAMES LAWRENCE

BED BUGS
TIM COLLINS & JAMES LAWRENCE

THE MIRROR
TIM COLLINS & JAMES LAWRENCE

THE LIFT
TIM COLLINS & ABBY RYDER

THIEF
TIM COLLINS & ABBY RYDER

Badger Publishing Limited, Oldmedow Road,
Hardwick Industrial Estate, King's Lynn PE30 4JJ

Telephone: 01438 791037
www.badgerlearning.co.uk

Bed Bugs 978-1-78837-419-4

2 4 6 8 10 9 7 5 3 1

Publisher / Senior Editor: Danny Pearson
Editor: Claire Wood
Series Consultant: Dee Reid
Designer: Fiona Grant
Cover Illustration: Mark Penman
Illustration: James Lawrence

Tim Collins

Illustrated by James Lawrence

Contents

Story Vocabulary
noisy
ceiling
wriggling

The story so far...

Arjun was lost in the woods. It was very foggy, but he could see a hotel in the distance.

"Welcome to Horror Hotel," said a woman. "I am the Manager. I hope you enjoy your stay with us."

Arjun didn't really want to stay in this strange hotel, but he knew it would only be for one night.

What could possibly go wrong? he thought.

Chapter 1

The Face

Arjun lay in bed.

He couldn't get to sleep.

The hotel was too noisy.

The floorboards creaked.

The pipes banged.

Arjun could hear someone crying in the room next door.

Arjun looked up at the ceiling.

There was something moving.

A small trapdoor was slowly opening.

Arjun saw a man's face looking down at him. He was covered in bugs.

The man gave an evil smile.

His long teeth were green with slime.

Chapter 2

The Mirror

Arjun turned on his bedside light.

The face and the trapdoor were gone.

Maybe they had never been there at all.

Now I will never get back to sleep, thought Arjun.

He got out of bed and went to the bathroom.

The sound of crying from the next
room was even louder.

Arjun turned on the tap.

The noisy pipes drowned out the crying.

Arjun washed his face in the sink.

He looked in the mirror.

There was a long cut across his face.

How did that happen? thought Arjun.

Arjun touched the cut and his skin
fell off in big clumps.

Arjun could see the bones of his face.

He screamed.

Chapter 3

Bed Bug

The door opened and the Manager walked in.

"What is the matter?" she asked. "Why are you screaming?"

"Look at my face!" shouted Arjun.

But when Arjun touched his face, there was no cut there at all.

"This hotel is evil," said Arjun.
"It is making me see things."

"I can help," said the Manager.

She took out a pair of tweezers
and pushed them into Arjun's ear.

He screamed with pain.

The Manager pulled a wriggling robot insect out of Arjun's ear.

"What is that?" asked Arjun. "It is disgusting!"

"It's a bed bug," said the Manager.

"You were lucky," said the Manager.
"If the bed bug got into your brain you
would see scary things for the rest of
your life."

"Let me out of here!" shouted Arjun.

Questions

Chapter 1

Why can't Arjun sleep? *(page 8)*

Why is the man scary? *(page 11)*

Chapter 2

What happens when Arjun turns on the bedside light? *(page 12)*

What does Arjun see when he looks in the mirror? *(page 18)*

Chapter 3

What does the Manager push into Arjun's ear? *(page 26)*

What would happen if the bed bug got into Arjun's brain? *(page 30)*

About the Author
Tim Collins has written over 90 books for adults and children.

He enjoys reading horror books and playing computer games.

He's stayed in lots of scary hotels, but none of them were haunted as far as he knows.

About the Illustrator
James Lawrence loves reading comic books.

He lives in Manchester and he spends his days drawing cool pictures.

He thinks he could survive a night at the Horror Hotel.